Contents

*B = bronze; S = silver; G = gold; non-bold type = descant/soprano recorder; bold type = treble/alto recorder.

Ready for a Rondo?

Brian Bonsor

AB 3135

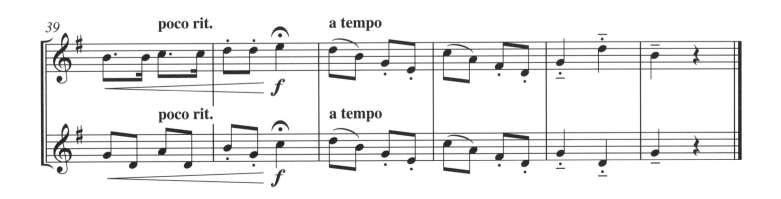

Strolling

Michael Rose

AB 3135

Dr Jekyll and Mr Hyde

Pam Wedgwood

Saraband for a Sad Salad

David Moses

AB 3135

Rag Bag

Sarah Watts

The Scarecrow

Jonathan Leathwood

AB 3135

The Willow Tree Bends in the Wind

Sally Adams

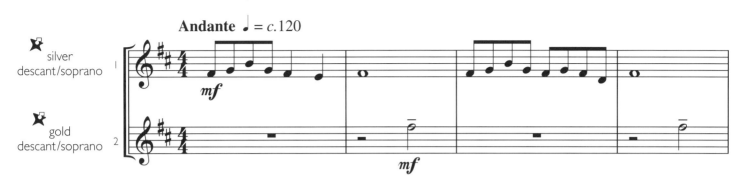

Punchlines

Jane Sebba

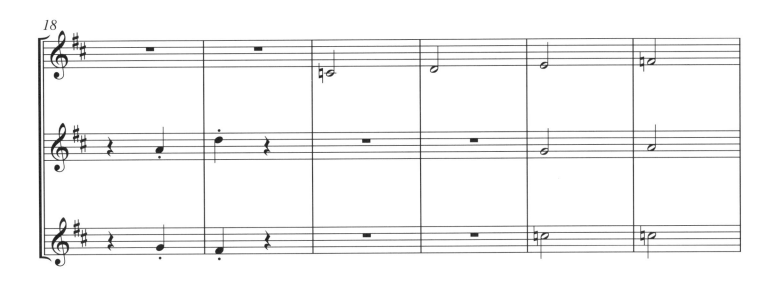

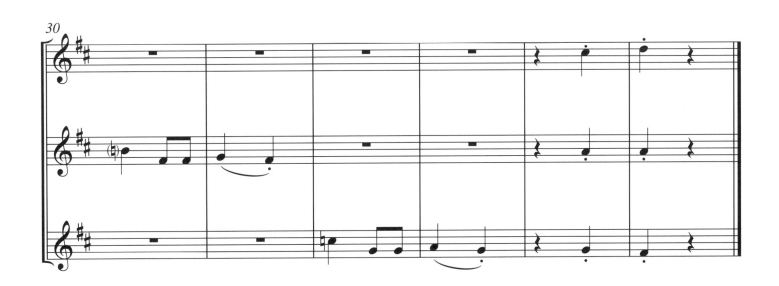

for Bethia

English Cadence

Robert Tucker

AB 3135

Watching the Clouds

Brian Bonsor

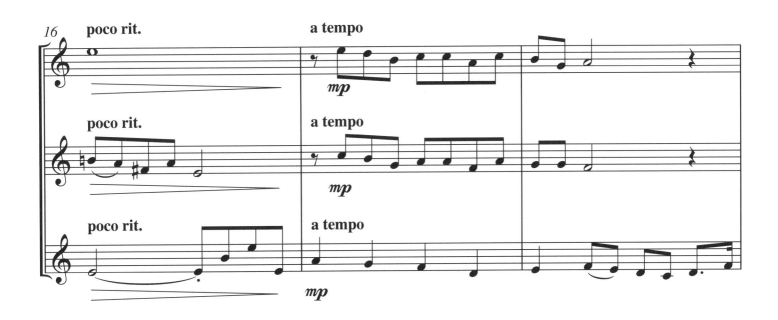

Waltz for Wednesdays

Sarah Watts

AB 3135

Clock Piece

Paul Harris

Take it Somewhere Different

Sarah Watts

AB 3135

My love's an arbutus

Trad. Irish *arr. Sally Adams*

AB 3135

Pony Ride

Brian Bonsor

AB 3135

All in a garden green

Trad. English arr. Alyson Lewin

Lord Willobie's Welcome Home

Trad. English arr. Alyson Lewin